ABC

Franklin Watts Incorporated

Brian Wildsmith

© Brian Wildsmith 1962

First published 1962 by Oxford University Press

First American publication 1963 by Franklin Watts, Inc.
575 Lexington Avenue, New York, N.Y. 10022

Library of Congress Catalog Card Number: 63 — 7131

Brian Wildsmith's ABC, a child's passport to the
world of letters, ranks high not only with small
children but with expert judges—librarians, re-
viewers, teachers. In the United States it has
been chosen by the American Library Association
for its list of Outstanding Books of 1963; by the
New York Public Library for exhibit and listing
in its 1963 booklet, Children's Books Suggested
as Holiday Gifts; and by The New York Times
Book Review's "Ten Best Illustrated Books of
1963." It has also been specially exhibited by the
Library of Congress.

In Great Britain in 1963, the Kate Greenaway
Award, comparable to the Caldecott Medal in the
United States, was given to Brian Wildsmith's
ABC.

SBN 531-01525-4

Printed in the United States of America

Sixteenth Printing

apple

APPLE

butterfly

BUTTERFLY

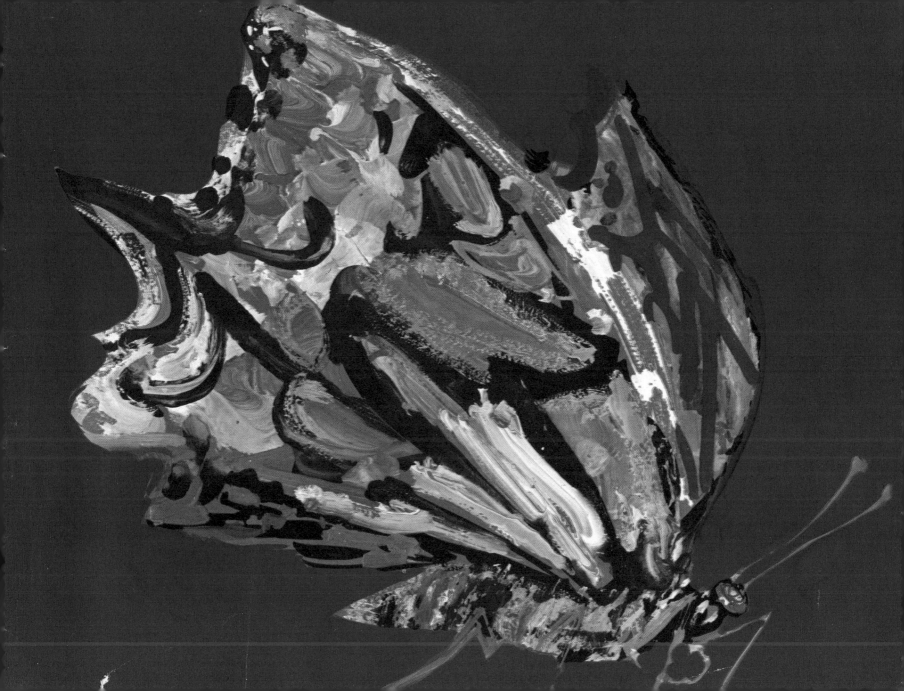

cat

CAT

dog

DOG

elephant

ELEPHANT

fish

FISH

goat

GOAT

horse

HORSE

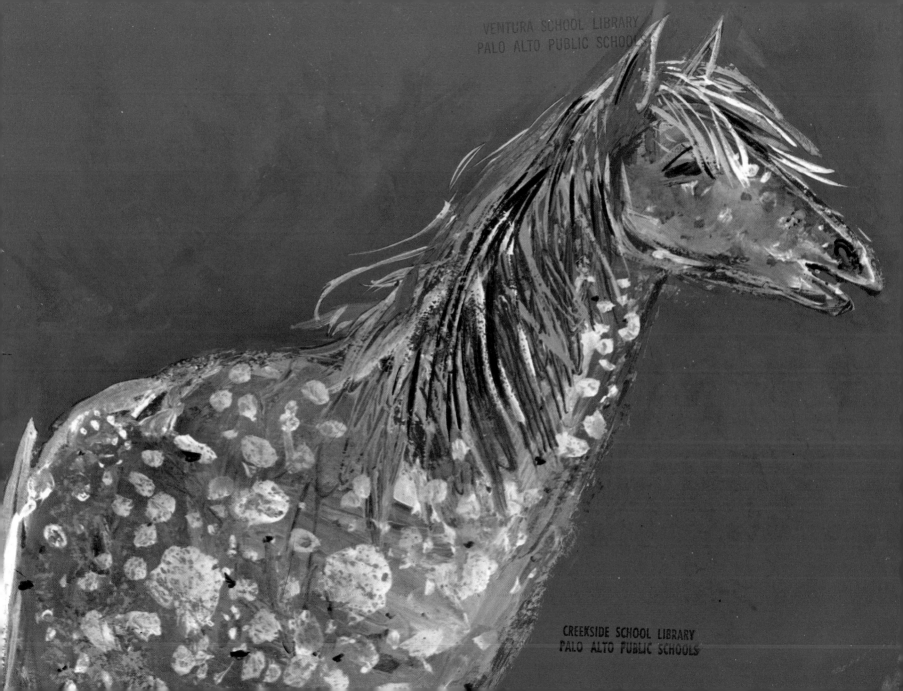

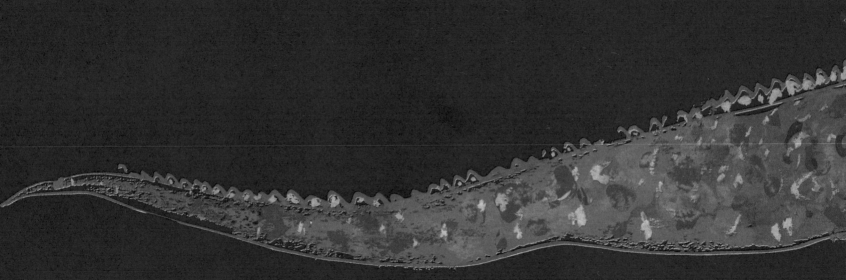

jaguar

JAGUAR

kettle

KETTLE

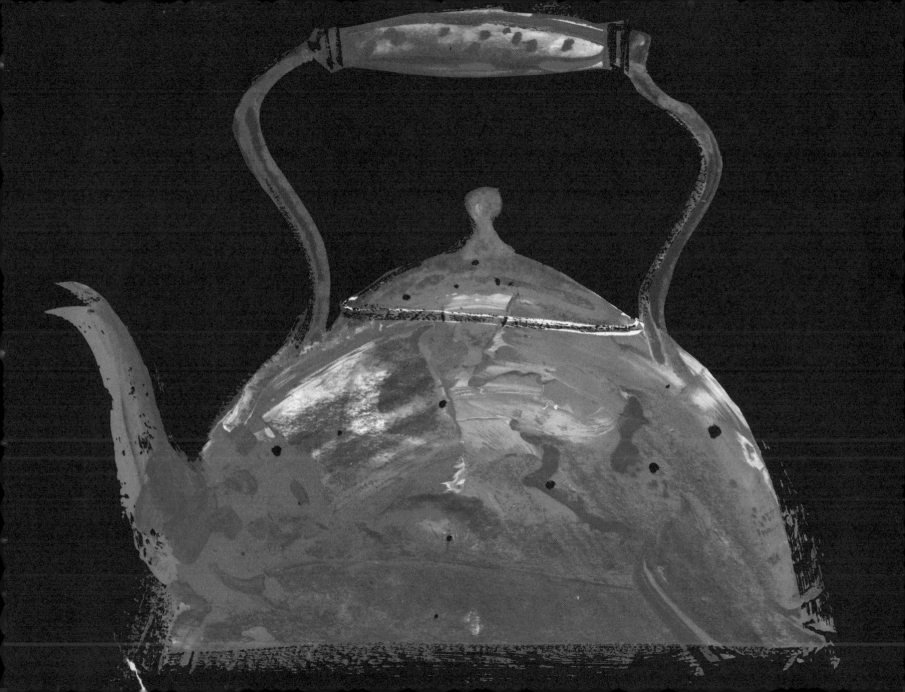

lion

LION

mouse

MOUSE

nest

NEST

owl

OWL

peacock

PEACOCK

queen

QUEEN

rooster

ROOSTER

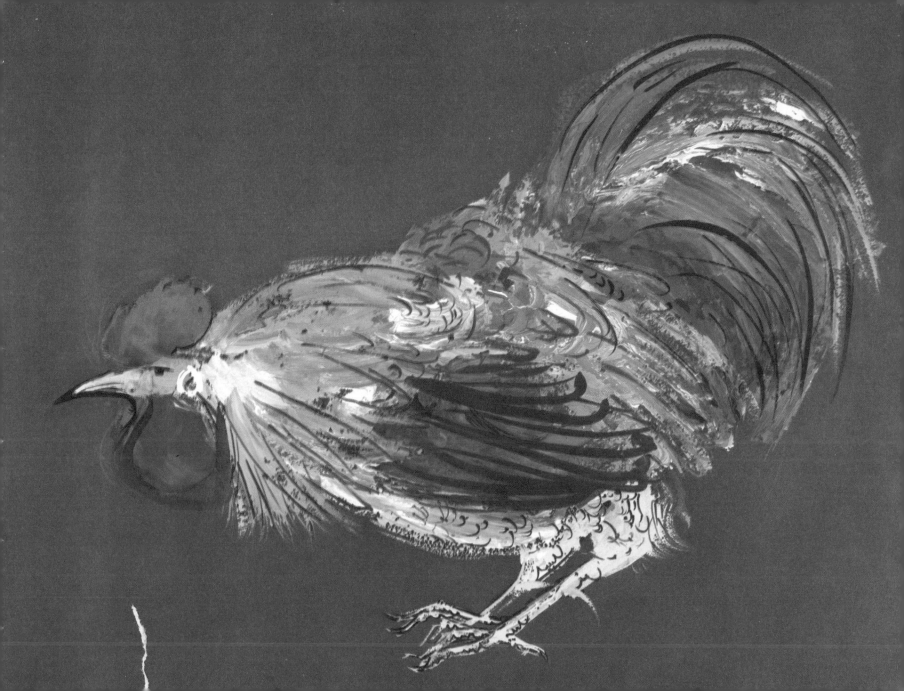

snail

SNAIL

turtle

TURTLE

unicorn

UNICORN

violin

VIOLIN

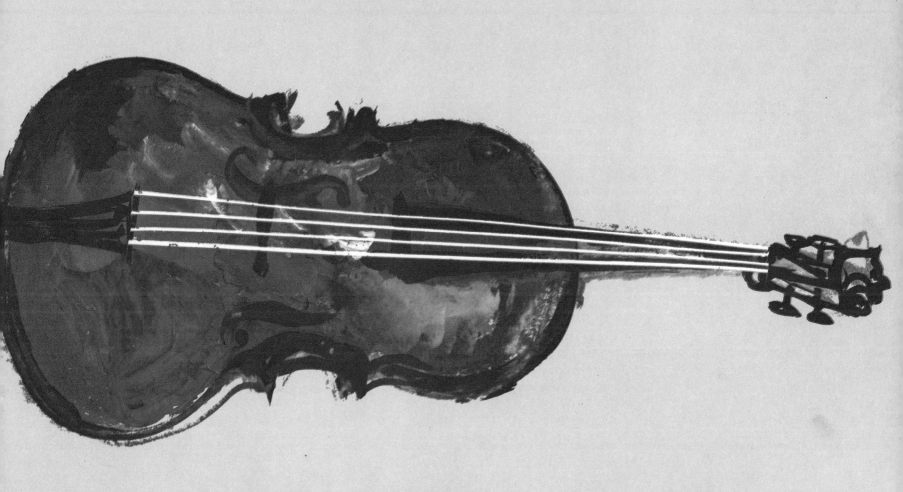

windmill

WINDMILL

xylophone

XYLOPHONE

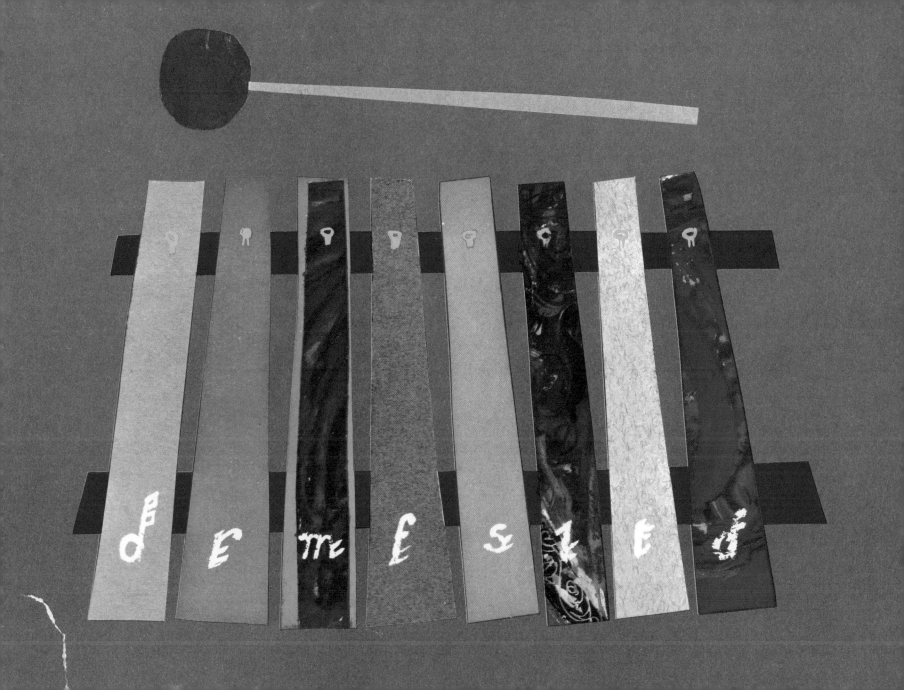

yak

YAK

zebra

ZEBRA

A is for apple.	N is for nest.
B is for butterfly.	O is for owl.
C is for cat.	P is for peacock.
D is for dog.	Q is for queen.
E is for elephant.	R is for rooster.
F is for fish.	S is for snail.
G is for goat.	T is for turtle.
H is for horse.	U is for unicorn.
I is for iguana.	V is for violin.
J is for jaguar.	W is for windmill.
K is for kettle.	X is for xylophone.
L is for lion.	Y is for yak.
M is for mouse.	Z is for zebra.

N O P Q R S T